Mum and Dad sat in the sun.

1

Kipper sat with them.

Biff and Chip were in the shed.

Chip had on a red, velvet jacket.

He had a box on his head.

"I am not Chip," he said.
"I am King Chip!"

Floppy ran and hid.

Biff had a red sash and a
big ring.

She had a long wig.

"I am not Biff," said Biff.
"I am Queen Biff!"

Biff got a shock.
"Floppy!" she said.

Then Floppy got a shock.
The wig fell on him.

The box fell down.

Then Chip and Biff fell down.

"Hush, Floppy!" said Mum.

"Look! Biff, Chip and Floppy are back!"